Cricket's Clubhouse

Written by

Robin Frederick and Jay Tverdak

Illustration by

Kathleen McCarthy

Cricket's World

Cricket's world is full of fun and activity for Cricket and <u>you</u>. There are five other Activity Book and Tape sets like this one. And Cricket also has her own great Outfits—each one comes with a special cassette tape, too.

Cricket Activity Books and Tapes

1. Cricket's Clubhouse
2. Growing Up With Cricket
3. Cricket Takes a Vacation
4. Around the World with Cricket
5. Cricket Goes Camping
6. Holiday Fun with Cricket

Cricket Outfits and Tapes

1. School Time
2. Time for Outdoor Fun
3. Party Time
4. Indoor Play Time
5. Sleepy Time
6. Time for Health and Exercise

Hi, this is Cricket talking to you! Are we going to have fun, or what?! There are so many things to do in this book, we better get started right away. You'll need crayons or felt pens, pencils, scissors, glue, tape and a few other things I'm sure you can find around the house.

Are you ready? Alright! Let's go!

It's time for a meeting at the clubhouse but I'm having trouble getting there. You can help me. Use your finger to trace the only path that will take me all the way to the clubhouse.

Well, here's the ol' clubhouse. But something doesn't look quite right. Can you find six things that are wrong with this picture? (The answers are on page 24 if you need 'em.)

My club is so special anyone can join...as long as you're a kid! You can make your own Official Member Badge.

Here's what you'll need:
  a piece of cardboard (you can cut up an empty cereal box)
  tape and glue
  crayons or felt pens
  a ball point pen
  a piece of paper

Cut a piece of cardboard about this size. Cut a piece of paper the same size and glue it to the cardboard. Trim the edges so they are even.

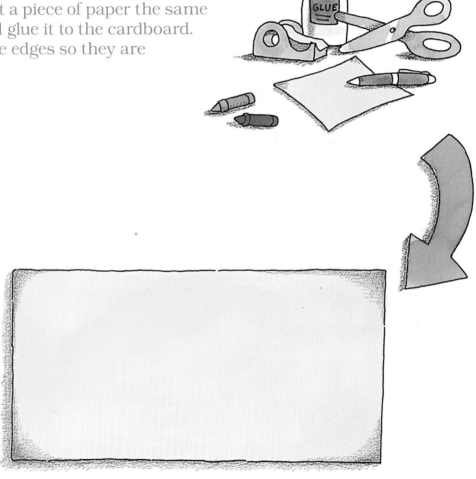

Now write your name and the words "CRICKET'S CLUBHOUSE" on your badge and decorate it with crayons or felt pens. But be sure to leave a space, like this:

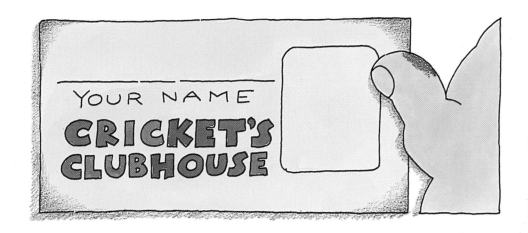

This is a place for your thumbprint. No two thumbprints are alike so putting your thumbprint on your Member Badge will identify y<u>ou</u> as a member of the club. Here's how you do it.
Color the top of your thumb with the ballpoint pen.

Now press your thumb onto the space on your Member Badge. Press hard and roll it from side to side. Don't rub your thumb on the paper or your print will smear. Now lift your thumb up and you'll see a clear thumbprint.

That's your Official Member Badge. Tape it to your shirt and now, <u>wash y</u>our thumb!

At every meeting, one person in the club is asked to bring in some-thing fun to do. Last week, it was my turn. I brought some paper and pencils and a mirror and we played a game. You can play it, too. Lay a piece of paper on a table in front of a mirror. Look in the mirror and move the paper until you can see it. Now, looking only in the mirror, draw a big "X". Now connect the corners to make a square. Hard, isn't it? Draw a tree. Draw a house. Now try to write your name. That's really hard!!!

Have you ever been bowling? It's lots of fun. We go bowling right here in the clubhouse. You can make your own bowling game.

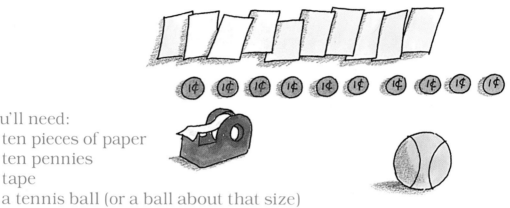

You'll need:
    ten pieces of paper
    ten pennies
    tape
    a tennis ball (or a ball about that size)

Roll up each piece of paper like this:

Tape it together. Then tape a penny to the bottom of each roll. These will be your bowling pins. Stand the pins up with the pennies on the bottom. Set them up like this.

Now stand across the room and roll the ball at the pins. See how many you can knock down with one roll. Give yourself a point for each pin you knock down. If you knock them all down in one roll that's called a "strike"! Give yourself ten extra points!

I brought some toys to share with the other club members this week but now I can't find them. You can help me. Find the eight toys hidden in the clubhouse.

I always bring some of my Mom's old magazines to the clubhouse. There are lots of things you can do with old magazines. Sometimes I just cut out a picture I like and hang it on the wall. Here's something else to do—make a mobile.

Here's what you'll need:
old magazines
2 wire coat hangers
string
glue
scissors

Fit one coat hanger inside the other, crosswise.

Tie them together at the top and at the bottom. Cut out small pictures that you like from the magazines

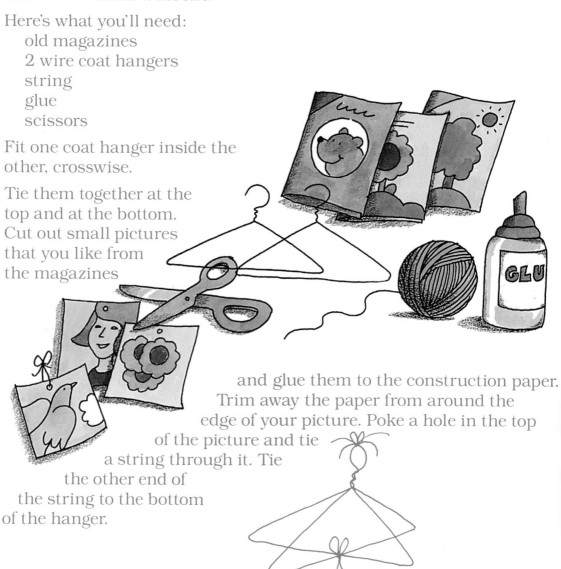

and glue them to the construction paper. Trim away the paper from around the edge of your picture. Poke a hole in the top of the picture and tie a string through it. Tie the other end of the string to the bottom of the hanger.

Use different lengths of string and space out your pictures so that each hangs freely. Now tie some string to the top of the coat hangers and hang your mobile up.

Sometimes we raise money for our club by selling lemonade. Here is a picture of our lemonade stand. There are six things in this picture that begin with the letter "D." Can you find them? (If you can't, the answers are on page 24.)

Here's something else you can do with old magazines—make a picture puzzle!

Here's what you'll need:
    old magazines
    construction paper
    glue
    scissors

Cut a page from a magazine with one big picture on it. It helps if the picture has several large things in it that are <u>not</u> the same color. Now glue a piece of construction paper to the back of the magazine page. Trim away any extra paper. Cut up the whole thing into 10 or 12 pieces. Now see if you can put them back together again!

IS THAT A PUZZLE OR WHAT?!

At the clubhouse we have lots of fun putting on puppet shows for each other. Here are some finger-puppets you can make.

You'll need:

paper you can trace with
crayons or felt pens
glue
scissors

Trace this picture of me and cut it out. Be sure to include the two bands that stick out from my legs.

Color the picture any way you want. Now hold it up against your first finger with the head towards your hand. Fit the bands around your finger so that they overlap, then glue them. Now you have a finger puppet. You can make more by tracing the ones on the next page.

Here's a silly story game we like to play at the clubhouse. You can play it, too. Here's how to do it. Read the story. Each time you come to a blank, close your eyes and point to a word in the circle. Then read the word you've chosen.

I am going to start a club, said Mike. It will be a _____ club for _____ people. I will ask all my _____ friends to join and we will have _____ refreshments and we will play _____ games. I hope you will join my club 'cause you're so _____

Quiet
sleepy
fussy
sloppy
jolly
grouchy
boring
noisy
gloomy
silly

Here's a fun drawing game for you to try.

You'll need:
    a book
    a pencil
    a piece of paper

Put the piece of paper on top of the book. Put the book on top of your head. Hold the book with one hand and with the other try to draw a picture of a girl, like this:

It isn't easy!

It isn't,
easy !

These two little girls look the same but they're not. Can you find five things about them that are different? Sure you can! (Just in case—the answers are on page 24.)

Here's a secret message from me to you.

To find out what it says you'll need:
    a piece of paper you can trace with
    a pencil

Trace the dark lines onto a piece of paper. Then fold the paper like this and read the message.

nswers:

Page 5.
1. No doorknob
2. Curtains are upside-down
3. Cat with two tails
4. Banana on apple tree
5. Cricket is misspelled "Kricket"
6. Wagon wheel missing

Page 9.
Dear Friend,
You are too good to be forgotten.
I will be seeing you.
      Love,
        Cricket

Page 12.
1. a top
2. a teddy bear
3. a doll
4. a rubber ball
5. a Jack-in-the-Box
6. a kite
7. a jump rope
8. a pogo stick

Page 16.
1. "DRINK"
2. Dog
3. "DAD"
4. Doll
5. Dress
6. Duck

Page 22.
1. one has pigtail ribbons
2. one has a pocket
3. one wears tennis shoes
4. one has polka-dot belt
5. one wears a necklace